What Is a Bat?

One day, the birds
and the animals
were playing a game of ball.
Bat wanted to play.

"Not on our side,"
said the birds.
"You have no feathers.
You're not a bird."

"Not on our side,"
said the animals.
"You have wings.
You're not an animal."

6

"I am an animal," said Bat.
"Look, I have teeth!"
The animals laughed.

The birds were winning.
When the ball went up high,
the birds could fly up
and catch it.

11

Bat wanted to help
the animals.
Next time the ball
went up high,
he flew up and caught it.

"Hey, Bat," said the birds,
"you can be on our side."

"No," said the animals,
"he has teeth.
He's an animal.
He can be on our side."

The animals won the game.
"We're glad you're
an animal, Bat," they said.